animals

Photography
George Siede and Donna Preis

Louis Weber, C.E.O.
Publications International, Ltd.
7373 N. Cicero Avenue
Lincolnwood, Illinois 60646

Manufactured in U.S.A. for the
publishers Peter Haddock Ltd.
Bridlington, England.

ISBN: 0-7105-0810-7

Publications International, Ltd.

dogs

cats

rabbits

ducks

budgerigars

penguins

chickens

raccoon

monkey

frog

toad

turtle

goats

pigs

butterflies

fish